Welcome fae The P...
So proud o' Malky's ...
Drawin's o' folk fae ...
There's even a Royal ...

The Big Yin's here tae make yiz laugh,
There's tales o' Scotland's glory.
Ally 'n' Andy wi' World Cup woes
But that's another story:

Thatcher, Kinnock, Gorby, Bush
A strange politic blend
But have nae fear Big Jim is here
Tae shore up Scotland's end

So sit yiz doon an' huvva laugh
Wee Malky's done yiz proud
Wan thing's fur sure, at any 'oor
His work will draw a crowd:

# The Cartoon Art of Malky McCormick

MAINSTREAM
PUBLISHING

First published in Great Britain in 1990 by
MAINSTREAM PUBLISHING COMPANY (EDINBURGH) LTD
7 Albany Street
Edinburgh EH1 3UG

**British Library Cataloguing in Publication Data**
McCormick, Malky
   McCormick : a collection.
   1. Scottish humorous cartoons
   I. Title
   741. 594
   ISBN 1 85158 357 2

Typeset in 10 on 12¹/₂pt Helvetica by The Graphics Company
Printed in Great Britain by Scotprint Ltd, Musselburgh

# CONTENTS

# ACKNOWLEDGEMENTS

Billy Connolly
*Daily Record*
*Evening Times*
*Golf Monthly*
*Kilmarnock Standard*
*Racing Post*
*Scottish Daily Express*
S.H.E.G.
*Sunday Mail*
*Sunday Telegraph*
*Sunday Times*

**Dedicated to**
**Ann, Dominic, Jane, Sean, Maw, Paw 'n' Mum**

# SCOTLAND...AYE...GUID

In the beginning when God was creating the world, he was sitting on cloud nine telling his pal the Angel Gabriel what he planned for Scotland. "Gabby," says he, "I'm going to give this place high majestic mountains, purple glens, streams laden with salmon, golden fields of barley from which a whisky-coloured nectar can be made, coal in the ground, oil under the sea...gas..." "Haudoan! Haudoan!" interjected the bold Gabriel. "Are you being too generous to these Scots?" Back came the Almighty Yin's reply, "Aye, but wait till you see the neighbours I'm giving them."

That may be legend, but the truth is Scotland is a wonderful country, stowed with great people, places and patter. Of course it's true, why else would so many of our good neighbours choose to visit us and forget the way home. But the Scots have also settled in foreign parts voluntarily or involuntarily ever since Culloden. The Prince himself travelled extensively after that event. Arisaig...Skye...Uist...Benbecula...in fact every which way but Lewis.

Throughout our land there is a warmth and pawky sense of humour. Take the road and the smiles to Dundee. Enjoy the northern delights of Aberdeen. Glasgow belongs to everyone. Then there's Embra, the city with a castle on the rocks and a concert hall to match. An American tourist remarked recently, "Gee, Elmer...ain't the Castle pretty, but why did they build it beside the railroad track?"

Not only the cities of Scotland, but the Borders, the Lowlands, the Highlands and Islands all possess their humour and characters.

"I have traivelled ower this country frae shore tae shining shore...Frae the swamps of Auchterderran tae the jungles o' Lochore." Witness the contrast and this only Fife!

So raise your glass to the Flower of Scotland! Slainte...We arra people. 'Natsafact.

# SEE GLASGOW...SEE CULTURE

At midnight 1st January 1990, Glasgow became intoxicated with Culture. Culture was coming out its ears. From the little cafés and bistros there were cries of "Gies merr o' that Culture, pal"..."Get some culture inty yir boady"..."Geeza wee Rachmaninov and a hauf pint"..."A large Johann Strauss".

For a whole year the good citizens were requesting screwtops of Chablis and caviare suppers. Where three ducks once winged their way across living-room walls, culture vultures now appeared. Wee dugs wandered The Merchant City with their noses in the air instead of where wee Glasgow dugs normally have their noses.

Punters in cultural wine bars sat around posing with their noses in the air... though maybe that was to prevent excess Chablis escaping. They discussed the merits of Vincent Van Gogh, Van de Velde and Hertz Van Rental, whose work they agreed was of a hire class.

At street parties throughout the city people who would normally "gie it laldy" became strangely sedate and proceeded to give it "Vivaldi". Those who previously wouldn't have known their arias from their Elgars were getting educated. None of your scabby sketches, pavement artists were producing abstract Picasso replicas...though maybe that was these wee guys full of Chablis again.

Sir John Geilguid soundalikes popped up in the glare of a solitary lamp-post to deliver endless monologues to a Hungarian goulash take-away...though that was mainly after closing time.

By the way, Culture City opening hours were so stretched that by the time one left a little taverna one couldn't actually see the works of art on offer.

Thousands squeezed into the SECC to hear Luciano Pavarotti, and by the time he got in, it was a squeeze. There's an awfy lotti Pavarotti.

A new concert hall was built and named after the city's illustrious leader "The Lally Palais".

Yes, it was one big arty farty party and all around the dear green place was an air of...*je ne sais quoi*...here maybe it was these wee guys with the Chablis and caviare suppers.

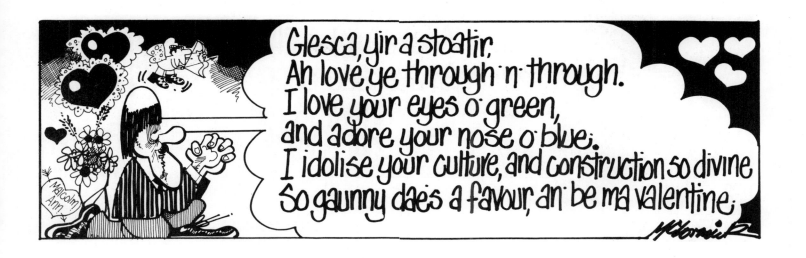

# GOOD HEALTH ???

Welcome to the wheezing, sneezing, slurping, burping, choking, boaking chapter.

The central character is The Dying Scotsman. Unlike The Flying Scotsman, our anti-hero frequently gets steaming and goes off the rails. Those close to him are none too chuff-chuff-chuffed by his anti-social behaviour.

We all know the character. He merely drinks to be sociable, but regularly gets as sociable as a newt. He habitually coughs up a fortune on cigarettes and at any suggestion of a keep-fit schedule, he'll run a mile. He says he's half-fit...the other fits in the grave.

He once attempted to give up smoking with the help of acupuncture. He claimed it worked well...when he inhaled, the smoke poured out all the wee holes, so he said.

Much to his long-suffering wife's displeasure he goes down to the pub most evenings and consumes several pints of contraceptive. She tries to be tolerant by gently pointing out to him the error of his ways. Tired of waiting up for his return from a day's drinking she'll leave a sarcastic note stating "Your supper's in the bottle" or hailing him in the morning with "Get up! Your breakfast's going flat!"

He does have a drink problem in that he only has one mouth. In the evenings he entertains the children with animal impressions...he drinks like a fish. He doesn't leave much of an impression on anyone else.

The character featured here was an infamous star of a press and television campaign run by the Scottish Health Education Group to make people more aware of the dangers of smoking, drinking and generally disregarding health and fitness.

Portrayed as a pathetic figure of mockery, he played his part as a warning against these dangers and subsequently society has definitely become more health conscious. But beware of complacency and remember, "The Dying Scotsman is alive and unwell and living on borrowed time."

"IF YOU WILL SOAK UP DRINK LIKE A SPONGE, NO WONDER I WIPE THE FLOOR WI' YOU"

"I THINK HE'S A TEST PILOT FOR THE NEW GLASGOW UNDERGROUND MOVIN' PAVEMENT"

"EVERY NIGHT HE'S ON THE BATTER...
NOO HE'S JIST ABOOT HAD HIS CHIPS"

"BE CAREFUL YE DON'T SPILL HIM"

"YOU WON'T NEED THAT, SON... YIR FAITHER TAKES
A BUCKET WHEREVER HE GOES"

"YOURS IS A RARE BLOOD GROUP...
90° PROOF"

"NO WONDER YOU FEEL WARM... YOU'VE THE PRICE OF 3 BAGS OF COAL INSIDE YOU"

"AH DON'T *THINK* IT'S PUB-SPY"

"IF YOU WANT ME TO BUY YOU A HAIR O' THE DOG...
YOU'RE BARKIN' UP THE WRONG TREE"

"HIS WIFE'S HELPIN' HIM TAE DRY-OOT... SHE WRUNG
HIS NECK LAST WEEK"

"AFTER A FEW HAIRS O' THE DOG, HE DEVELOPS AN AFFINITY FOR LAMPOSTS"

"AN' HE BOASTS HE TAKES HIS DRINK *STRAIGHT*"

"HE NEVER WEARS A BUNNET... A CORK WOULD FIT HIM BETTER"

"THEY CALL HIM THE GLASGOW OVERSPILL"

"AH HEAR YIR DAD DOES TRAIN IMPRESSIONS...
GETS STEAMIN' AN GOES AFF THE RAILS"

"HE CAME IN FOR A HAIR O' THE DOG AN' LEFT ON
ALL FOURS"

"I'M SUFFERIN' FROM ILLNESS AND FATIGUE... I'M SICK AND TIRED O' YE"

"HE DOESN'T DRINK MUCH... HE SPILLS MOST OF IT"

"THE DYIN' SCOTSMAN IS NO' WELL... AND WON'T BE APPEARING IN THIS ADVERTISEMENT"

"AND CIGARETTE SMOKERS DROP SUDDENLY"

"IT WORKS... WHEN YOU INHALE, THE SMOKE POURS OOT THE WEE HOLES"

# E II R INDOORS RULES U.K.

It's often said "See Royalty! You can keep them". Well, we do, in a manner to which we aren't accustomed.

There's a lot of them, a Family like an upper crust "Broons".

The head of them is a nice wee Scottish woman who bides in Grannie's Heilan' Hame reading the *Peoples' Friend* and *Racing Post*. Next there's Lizzie and her man Chooky (not Hen but Chooky Embra). She runs around being nice and waving to folk and it's all Greek to him.

The twins are gallus laddies - Chick and Andy. Chick wants to be "The King" but he isn't a patch on Sidney Devine. Andy hopes to go to sea one day...just for the day. Edward, the quiet one, just sits reading *Oor Wullie*.

The lassies get on well, the bonnie one and the frumpy one. Anne works hard so you never see her.

Then finally there's the bairns...dozens of them. They're friendly with her in Number 10, that's Glebe Street, not Downing Street.

They all spend holidays in the Highlands in a wee B & B (Balmoral and Braemar). One of the lassies (the bonnie one) says it's freezing and doesn't like it. Chick says little William gets cold, but that's only when he's wearing his kilt. Andy gets cold too, but he's got a wee pig to cuddle in bed.

The Family like to sit round the fire and have a wee sing song. The bonnie lassie sings:

> *Next year I'm off to Sunny Spain,*
> *So stuff you Britannia.*
> *I don't like Balmoral in the rain,*
> *Scotch Mist doesn't tan ya.*

Then they all launch into a medley of Family favourites..."Oh we do like to be beside the Deeside"..."Walking in a Windsor Wonderland"..."God save our Gracious team". Then Lizzie belts out a great version of "Bohemian Rhapsody".

They've a great life, but I wouldn't like their job.

# ORDER! ORDER!

Politicians of every hue irritate and annoy. Hence the cry "Bestuvorder Hues!"

They're controversial, bombastic and always right, so when they're wrong, the cartoonist sharpens his pencil, smiles wryly and murmurs to himself "Right!...they started it."

It has to be admitted that politicians supply an awful lot of material for satire. They do enjoy seeing themselves portrayed in cartoon form as it massages their egos. It also lets everyone see they're working at being awkward. It shows they are alive and well, though mainly living in Cloud Cuckooland...They also pay quite well for originals of themselves.

One collector of original drawings was a former Glasgow Lord Provost (El Pee) who enjoyed a weekly walk-on part in one of my cartoon strips. One occasion, however, he became displeased at what his comic equivalent had to say, and complained. He was even more displeased when his character was left out in future to save any bother.

Leaders foster caricaturable images of themselves to a ridiculous extent. Hitler's moustache...Churchill's cigars...Harold's Gannex...Scargill's sideburns...Thatcher's policies. Some haven't got it right though...Kinnock is all Welsh and freckles and Labour would do well to bring back the cartoonists' delight Michael Foot...Paddy Ashdown is pretty, David Steel is pretty dull and at the time of going to press, the SNP haven't elected a new leader, but he or she will be pretty good.

Of our own mob, would Malcolm Rifkind look the part with contact lenses? Would Donald Dewar have the same bite with new wallies? Would Baron Bampot (Nicholas Fairbairn) do the same dandy job wearing a boiler suit?

With TV in Parliament now, politicians are more readily recognisable to the public. Now less junior ministers have to be identified in cartoons with name tags on their coats or briefcases, but watch them sprout bum fluff on their upper lips, wear monocles or cultivate large red noses in order to be portrayed as characterful.

Large red noses are a must in that Great British Cartoon Gallery in London...The House of Lords. And did you know it was one of them that gave his title to the term for comic text...a speech balloon?

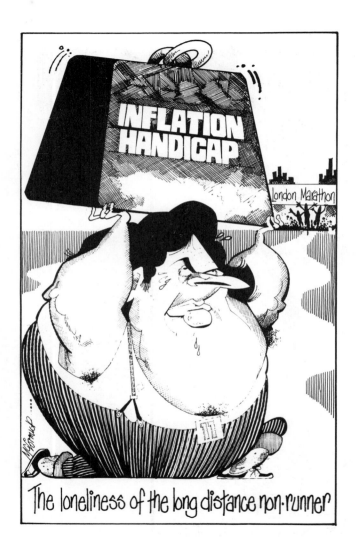

The loneliness of the long distance non-runner

Passing the bucks

Got it George? Don't do as I did... ..Do as Margaret says

# FIVE-IN-A-ROW

"Yabbadabba do...and it's easy". Well it wasn't and it hasn't been since.

In 1974 the Scottish national football team embarked on an epic five-in-a-row World Cup expedition. The Tartan Army was on the march. Nae Borra, it's a daudle.

Wee Willie Ormond was the Commander in Chief who led us in 1974 to West Germany (as opposed to East Germany, but nowadays, what does it matter, as its aw wan?). We performed well against Zaire, Yugoslavia and Brazil and returned to a heroes' welcome. We hadn't actually won anything, but hurray, we were unbeaten!

1978 saw the troops with a new General and we were on the move again to Argentina as Ally's Army. Ally McLeod is a nice man and unfairly condemned for the debacle that followed. Iran! Peru! sounded together like Scotland's other national drink and they sure left us with one gigantic hangover. We won a game against Holland and returned to an anti-heroes' welcome.

1982 and we were off to Sunny Spain, Oh Viva Caledonia! This time we were led by the Big Man, Jock Stein. After Ally's over-optimistic approach, Jock was enlisted to keep our feet on the ground, but with our heads in the clouds we were more than ten feet tall again. We had a dream but we weren't good enough against Brazil, New Zealand or Russia and returned home.

Our trip to Mexico in 1986 was a complete waste of time and the best thing about this campaign was our cartoon World Cup mascot McTex! One solitary goal by Gordon Strachan against West Germany was all we had to cheer about. We didn't do much against Denmark or Uruguay. Alex Ferguson was our stand-in manager and he was not outstanding. Like the Grand Old Duchess of York our Fergie marched us up to the top of the hill and marched us down again.

And so to Italia '90. This time Andy Roxburgh was "The Beak" in charge. He took a workmanlike team to Italy and they did a workmanlike job. Well he hadn't much to "pick" from. Gubbed by Costa who?, we then beat Sweden but were robbed by Brazil and sent homewards to think again.

It's not a great record, we know.

But then we do know...'cos we were there.

"WHIT D'YE MEAN HE HASNY HAD MUCH LUCK...
HE MISSED ARGENTINA, DIDN'T HE?"

"EFTER ARGENTINE, THEY'LL HUV TAE GIE ME
A LOT MERR THAN THAT TAE FOLLOW THEM"

"IF YE THINK RA HOLY GRAIL WIZ ELUSIVE...
WAIT TILL YE SEE JOHN ROBERTSON"

"UR YE SURE YE NEED AW THIS LUGGAGE JIST
TAE GO TAE IBROX FUR RA NEW YEAR AULD
FIRM MATCH?"

**"WHO DO WE PLAY IN THE FINAL?"**

**"THE OPENIN' GAME WILL BE PLAYED WITH THE DRAW ORGANISER'S HEID"**

**"SPAIN WILL PLAY..."**

**"AH'M HOPIN' THEY BEAT EACH OTHER"**

"IF THE WHOLE TEAM CAN WALK ON WATER SO CAN I"

"...NOT BY TORRALTA, TORRALTA OR TORRALTA.... WE SHALL NOT BE MOVED"

"HE CANNY BEAR TAE WATCH THE BRAZIL GAME"

"BRAZIL'S GOT A SECRET WEAPON... IT'S CALLED SUNSHINE"

"I THOUGHT WE WERE ONLY GAUN TAE SPAIN FUR A FORTNIGHT?"

"WHAT YOU THEENK 'EENY MEENY MINEY MO' MEANS, PEDRO?"

"IT OBVIOUSLY DIZNY MEAN HANSEN"

"THE WANS NO' INJURED HUV DEFECTED"

"WHERE WE GOING, WHERE WE GOING, WHERE WE GOING?"

"THEY'RE SEGREGATIN' US... THE
WANS GAUN TAE MEXICO AN'
THE WANS NO"

# FITBA' CRAZY

Let's raise our glasses and say "Cheers" to Scottish club football. With Tennents and Skol heavily into sponsorship verily doth our cups overflow. Dundee United have Belhaven all down the front of their shirts. Rangers have officially abandoned their traditional tipple of bitter orange for McEwan's Lager. The number of exports from England who've joined Rangers may make Bass a more appropriate sponsor. Then having in recent years accumulated a number of championship medals, Rangers shirt slogan could read "Gongs Ya Bass". Great rivals Celtic, though not sponsored by brewers, obviously have nothing against a few glasses...though not rose-tinted ones.

There was a time when youngsters were proud to wear continental names on their football jerseys like Real Madrid or Real Sociedad. Now it appears Real Ale goes down better. Motherwell have body-swerved the booze and are associated with the Scottish Health Education Group. Strange one...even though "The Well" are on a health kick they're still "Skelly" every Saturday.

By the way, there's a Sunday League in Glasgow that boasts such illustrious names as A.C. Milanda, Third Lanliq and Crystal Palates, a team of dental students.

The biggest revolution in Scottish club football has been the influx of foreign players to the game. We now have Englishmen, Dutchmen, Poles, Israelis and Irish playing every week. Kilmarnock FC went overseas to sign a youngster from Millport. The lad tackles like a crocodile and is solid as a rock.

Graeme Souness started it all with the transformation at Ibrox and performed the miracle of enticing Mo Johnston to Rangers when all he wanted to do was play for "the only club for me"...Celtic. Shock! Horror! Outrage...burning of scarves, threats...even to the player himself. Mo said he was over the moon, some suggested he might be safer staying up there. He sought sanctuary in the East, probably The Bass Rock, where there ain't much to do but there's lots of birds.

Anyway, things worked out for Mo and Rangers, and the whole of Scottish football is richer with the coming of our foreign friends...but don't tell that to Andy Roxburgh!!!

"NOT BY IRELAND, NORWAY OR AUCHENSHUGGLE, WE SHALL NOT BE MOVED"

"THERE'S THE SCOTTISH TEAM BUS"

"IS THERE ANY CHANCE O' BANNIN' US FAE HAMPDEN TAE?"

"WATCHIN' SCOTLAND NOO WULL BE LIKE GETTIN' A LEG AFF WITHOOT ANAESTHETIC"

"POOR SOWELS... THEY'LL NOW HUFTY STERT
WATCHIN' SCOTLAND LIKE THE REST O' US"

"AYE, THERE'S ALWAYS SOMEONE WORSE AFF THAN YIRSEL"

"LET'S LOOK AGAIN AT HOW WELL ORGANISED IN ATTACK OUR ENGLISH HOOLIGANS ARE"

**"I CAN'T REMEMBER HOW MANY POINTS YOU GET FOR A WIN AT PRESENT"**

**"WHEN THEY ASK FUR A HAUF O' CHAMPAGNE AN' A POKE O' CAVIARE CRISPS, YE KNOW THEY'RE OOT RA HABIT O' CELEBRATIN"**

"AH ONCE SAVED AN AULD MAN FAE BEIN' MUGGED... AH CONTROLLED MASEL"

"I TOLD THEM TO JIST GO OUT THERE AN' ENJOY THEMSELVES"

"NOO WE CAN CONCENTRATE WUR EFFORTS ON QUALIFYIN' FUR THE LATTER STAGES O' RA GLESCA CUP"

"AH PREFERRED THE OLD STAND WHERE YE HARDLY SAW RA MATCH"

"AH STILL PREFER MA PIE AN' BOVRIL TAE YON CAVIARE"

"PLEASE... PLEASE LEAVE ME OOT TOO"

"AN' IF ATTENDANCES KEEP FALLIN' AT IBROX... THEY CAN SCRAP THOSE FANCY SEATS AN' INSTALL A 3-PIECE SUITE"

"YE CANNY TELL WHICH FANS UR WHICH... THEY'VE AW GOT BLUE NOSES"

"YIR RIGHT IT'S FOGGY... THIS IS PARKHEID, NO' GOVAN"

"AW NAW... NO' ANITHER SEASON ALREADY"

"IT'S SO BAD AH WIZ CAUTIONED FUR TACKLIN' A PIE AT HAUF TIME"

"THE LOSERS RECEIVE WAN THOOSAND FAGS, A BOATTLE O' WHISKY AN' A GREASY FISH SUPPER... EACH"

"I DEMANDED MY TRUE WORTH AN' HE SAID 'OKAY WOULD YOU LIKE IT HEADS OR TAILS?'"

"ACCORDING TO THE CARDS, YOU'RE GOING ON A SHORT JOURNEY FOR A LONG TIME IN THE IMMEDIATE FUTURE"

"THERR'S OOR MR. SUPERFIT... RA ITHER FIT'S HOPELESS.

"AN' IF YOU DON'T ADOPT A MERR PASSIVE TOLERANT ATTITUDE AH'LL KICK YIR BACKSIDE AW OWER RA PARK."

"TODAY'S TEAM IS D. WILKIE, D. DUCK, J. COUSTEAU..."

"SHAME WE AIN'T GOT THE CONQUERIN' BIT RIGHT, TREV"

"NAME PLEASE... JIST AFORE YE GO"

"ACH IT WOULDNY WORK...'BONNIE UNITED KINGDOM OF GREAT BRITAIN AN' NORTHERN IRELAND. WE'LL SUPPORT YOU EVERMORE' DIZNY SCAN"

# WHAT'S THE GAME?

I once applied for the post of manager with my local football team Fenwick Tattiehowkers AFC. When asked what managerial experience I had, I replied, "None, but I'm used to working with comics." I didn't get the job but following the team develops my sense of humour.

Football and sport in general is a funny old game. It's as old as Adam 'n' Eve and they were game, though after a few apple ciders, Adam's keepie-uppy let him down.

The first spectator sport was The Lions versus Christians fixture but it became a bit predictable, with the Christians frequently losin' the heid. Can you imagine their manager's pre-match team talk? "Be patient lads, and just go out there and enjoy yourselves." The boys done not well at all.

Scotland-England sporting encounters through the ages have always been fiercely contested in such venues as Hampden, Murrayfield, Barrowland, Bannockburn and Drumclog. The visiting team – demoralised by such wild tribal Celtic slogans as: Intyrum! Intyrum!...Geezaboady!...Hackimdoon!...Yabassa! – invariably fled before kick off. One notable exception was Culloden where chants of "Five foot two, eyes of blue, Bonnie Prince Charlie's after you" didn't intimidate our opponents one bit.

The present trend in sport is to indoor games like snooker, darts and dominoes. These are bar-room games that require you to start with a double and probably a couple of pints, twenty fags and a poke of crispy fries.

Other indoor pursuits nowadays are watching golf on the telly, viewing athletics on the box, playing football videos or merely sitting there wondering why the same two teams contest the Boat Race Final every single year.

Rugby's a hilariously funny old game too. After the Grand Slam decider 1990, wasn't Scotland laughing up its sleeve and England laughing on the other side of its face. Ha! Ha! Ha!

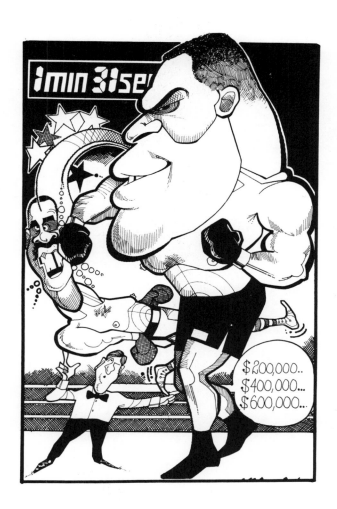

**"THEY MUST'VE BEEN SLEEP-WALKIN"**

"SO ROMANTIC... LISTEN HE'S SWEARING HIS UNDYING LOVE"

"IT'S LIKE ITALIAN FITBA'... YIV TAE TRY AN' KEEP RA BAW OOT RA NET"

"NO! BORG DOES NOT GET WIMBLEDON TO KEEP IF HE WINS AGAIN"

"IT'S NO' VERY STEEP!"

"IF THE WEST INDIANS BOWLED THIS WAY,
ENGLAND MIGHT SCORE A RUN OCCASIONALLY"

"IT'S SOME SPECIAL EVENTS FOR THE
AFGHANISTAN TEAM"

"PERSONALLY, AH WISH HE'D BREK AW SIDNEY
DEVINE'S RECORDS NEXT"

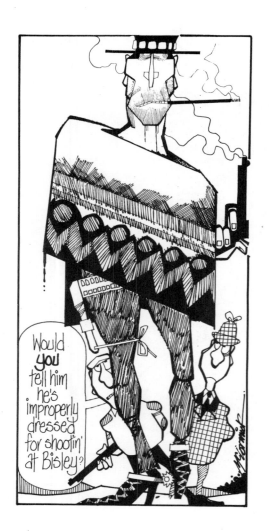

# SONGS YA BASS

The Scottish entertainment scene is in good shape. With comedians like Fran 'n' Anna and Sydney Devine around, you have to laugh. The two lovable lassies from Pont-du-Cote (Coatbridge, ya eejits!) were recently awarded British Empire Medals – now they can promote themselves as a pair of BEMpots. Not many people realise that the gruesome twosome were the inspiration behind Robert Burns' poem "The Twa Dogs".

It was thought Sydney Devine was seeking a new image when he was seen wearing the kilt. He denied this saying it was an attempt to re-release his "Tiny Bubbles". To mark a decade of Thatcherism, Sydney plans an over-optimistic anthem entitled "When you on high were hung, Maggie".

In the television world "The Beechgrove Garden" continues to flourish and one recent programme was highly educational and entertaining. It was called "Grow your own dope...Plant an Englishman". Open days at the garden remain ever popular and the other week in the vegetable plot there was a very big turnup.

On the other side "The High Road" should really "Take The High Jump" and while "Taggart" is a top cop show, the chief inspector is to acting what the Munich Beer Festival is to the Queen Mother's social diary.

Rab C. Nesbitt and his Naked Video team are simply the best. Naked Video always seems to be over in a "flash" though. Talking of flashing, old Jumping Jock along with his fellow stones rolled into Hampden to perform for Culture Year. One of their classic numbers was dedicated to unhappy Ayr United fans with Mick beseeching them "Hey, youze, get aff McLeod!"

Across the city at Ibrox Stadium old bluenose Sinatra wooed 'em with "Rangers in the Night". There were a few strangers there too...some Scottish players.

Continuing the trend of showbiz spectaculars at football grounds it's been suggested that the Pope at Parkhead may add a bit more needed polish.

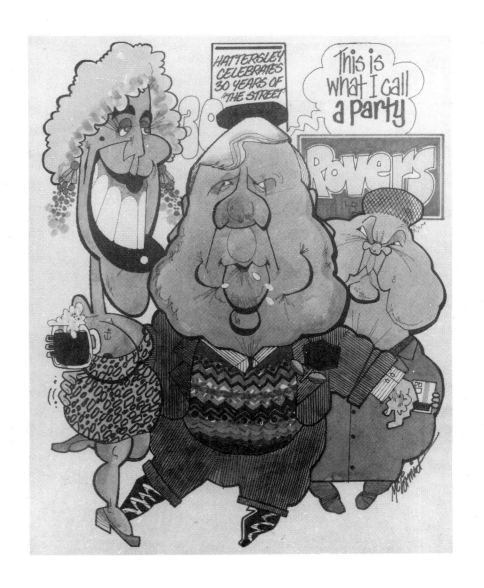

# THE BIG YIN

"Hullo! Howzitgaun?" This section is special because "The Big Yin" cartoon strip was unique and an important break in my career in 1975.

The action was set in any part of Glasgow where "Wur Hero" (Billy Connolly in disguise) weaved his way about with his china, "The Wee Man", commenting on world events such as the increase in price of "tuppenny-mop-up" to 50p a glass.

A favoured rendezvous was "The Sorry Heid", with its varied gantry...Blackhill Beaujolais...Nuits St Georges Cross...Sotsmac (The Bam's Dram)...El Dee and Bam-brusco. These tipples were dispensed by two buxom brammirs, Mona Lang and Leeza Lane though not to resident drunk Englebert Humfyirdrink, who was regularly oxtered into the bar. The Big Yin would occasionally depart the pleasures of Glasgow and venture on a missionary expedition to Embra, where, during Festival time, he noted the one o'clock gun went "Poof!" instead of "Bang".

He would sail forth to Arn (haudoan, Arn izny inra Forth, its inra Clyde!). On Arn he commented "How izaat Goat Fell?!!...Naw he's just a wee bit unsteady on his feet. He ventured to Wembley, Rossy, Brassy and had a pal who was abroad once but got a sex change.

Real and imagined characters frequented the strip...Pastor Glass, a real pane, you can see right through him. There was Lord Lucan who may still be hiding in the Partick Thistle trophy room with Shergar and Salman Rushdie. Naturally The Queen would pop in for her messages...20 Regal King Size, some King Edwards and Queen Victorias.

There was Badyin McFadyin the Corporation bus driver whose famous stunt was to drive his double decker over 15 motorcycles. The theme tune of local convict Tam the Bam was "Roll out the Bar L" and he enjoyed a jail-bird's eye view of Riddrie from his window. PC Owen Yirway was always after him.

Both "The Big Yin" cartoon character and Billy himself are featured here as a wee tribute to the definitive verbal cartoonist...Orrabest, Pal.

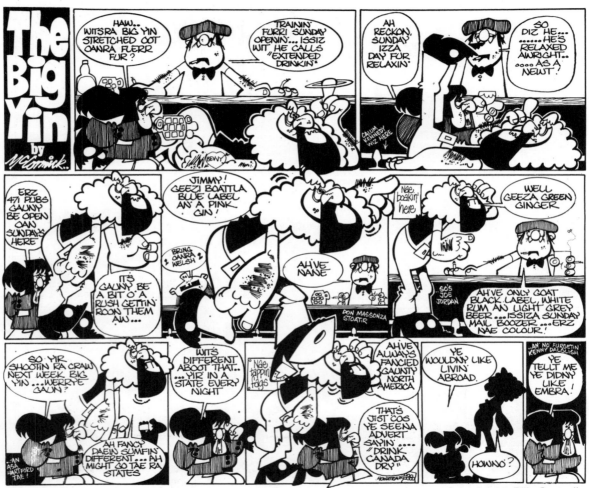

# GENERAL JOKES 'N' JAPES

Bits 'n' pieces...odds 'n' sods...pick 'n' mix...this 'n' that... chit 'n' chat...here 'n' there...sticks 'n' stones...mish 'n' mash...up 'n' down...roon 'n' roon...little 'n' large...erse fr' elbow...mince 'n' tatties...way 'n' jump. This chapter is all of these. A graphic goulash mixture to feast yourself on. A kind of 57 varieties of rhubarb, raspberries and sour grapes, sweetened occasionally with crème de la crème. A blend not to be trifled with. It's a cartoon curry of red herrings. has beans and currant affairs — hot stuff to get your teeth into.

A pen 'n' pencil paella, stirred up and dished out with a big spoon.

You have set before you a general melée of jokes, japes, jookerie pookerie and jargon not to mention tomfoolery and mummery delivered with the subtlety of a custard pie.

It's a pure ham 'n' corn omelette.

We all know you can't make an omelette without breaking eggs, consequently eggs anxious to appear in this production were heard to cry, "Geeza break! Geeza break!" Fools. don't they know nobody gets a break in this book?

Whatever your taste in humour there's something from McCormick's palette to titillate your palate. Tasty titbits...meaty comments...roasted nuts...stewed prunes...grilled politicians and minced dumplings.

The purveyor of this 2B or not 2 Beanfeast is also the man listed in *Who's Who?* as Who? The man a wee Glasgow wummin described as being a better drawer than a breid poltice. So draw up a chair and help yourself to some of Malky's Minestrone... with a little glass of Bo-Jolly.

"...MUST BE WHERE AWRA BUMS HING OOT"

"AH CAUGHT HIM IN THE TILL, AND HE SAID HE THOUGHT THE CHANGE WOULD DO HIM GOOD"

"THAT'S WHIT AH LIKE ABOOT GAUN ABROAD, THAE CONTINENTALS MAKE YE FEEL AT HAME"

"AH TELLT YE IT WIZ FREEZIN"

"AH HEARD THEY ASKED FUR SOMETHIN' EXTRA IN THEIR PAY PACKETS, AN' GOT A WEE PLASTIC SUBMARINE EACH"

"IT'S MERR COMPLICATED ALREADY...YE JIST USED TAE HUFTY VOTE 'X' "

Ahim jist a wee sparra.
Ahim froze tae ra marra.
Ahim knackered an' jist aboot deid.
Ahve nuthin' tae peck,
So please geeza brek
An' fling me a big dod o' breid

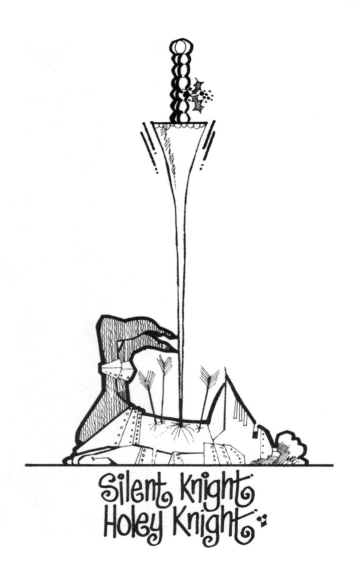

Silent Knight
Holey Knight